Engaging Math with Activities 1

CHANDRIKA JAINI VEDAM
EX-LECTURER AHLCON PUBLIC SCHOOL

Edited by
Gunjan Singh
M.A., B.Ed.

Early Childhood Mathematics Education

WISEMEN PUBLICATIONS
WISEMEN Creative Education Pvt. Ltd.
83, 2nd Floor, Shyamlal Marg, Daryaganj, New Delhi-110002
info@wisemenpublications.com

Count and Colour

One Snowman

Trace and write :

1 1 1 1 1 1 1

1 1 1 1 1 1 1

1 1 1 1 1 1 1

1 1 1 1 1 1 1

Count and Colour

Trace and write :

2 2 2 2 2 2 2

2 2 2 2 2 2 2

2 2 2 2 2 2 2

2 2 2 2 2 2 2

Trace and write :

3 3 3 3 3 3 3

3 3 3 3 3 3 3

3 3 3 3 3 3 3

3 3 3 3 3 3 3

Count and Colour

Trace and write :

4 4 4 4 4 4 4

4 4 4 4 4 4 4

4 4 4 4 4 4 4

4 4 4 4 4 4 4

Count and Colour

Trace and write :

5 5 5 5 5 5 5

5 5 5 5 5 5 5

5 5 5 5 5 5 5

5 5 5 5 5 5 5

Colour the number names. Then write them again in the space provided.

ONE ....

TWO ....

THREE ....

FOUR ....

FIVE ....

Colour the following numbers.

1 2 3 4 5

Circle 3 balls in these.

Draw and colour 4 balloons below.

Count and Colour

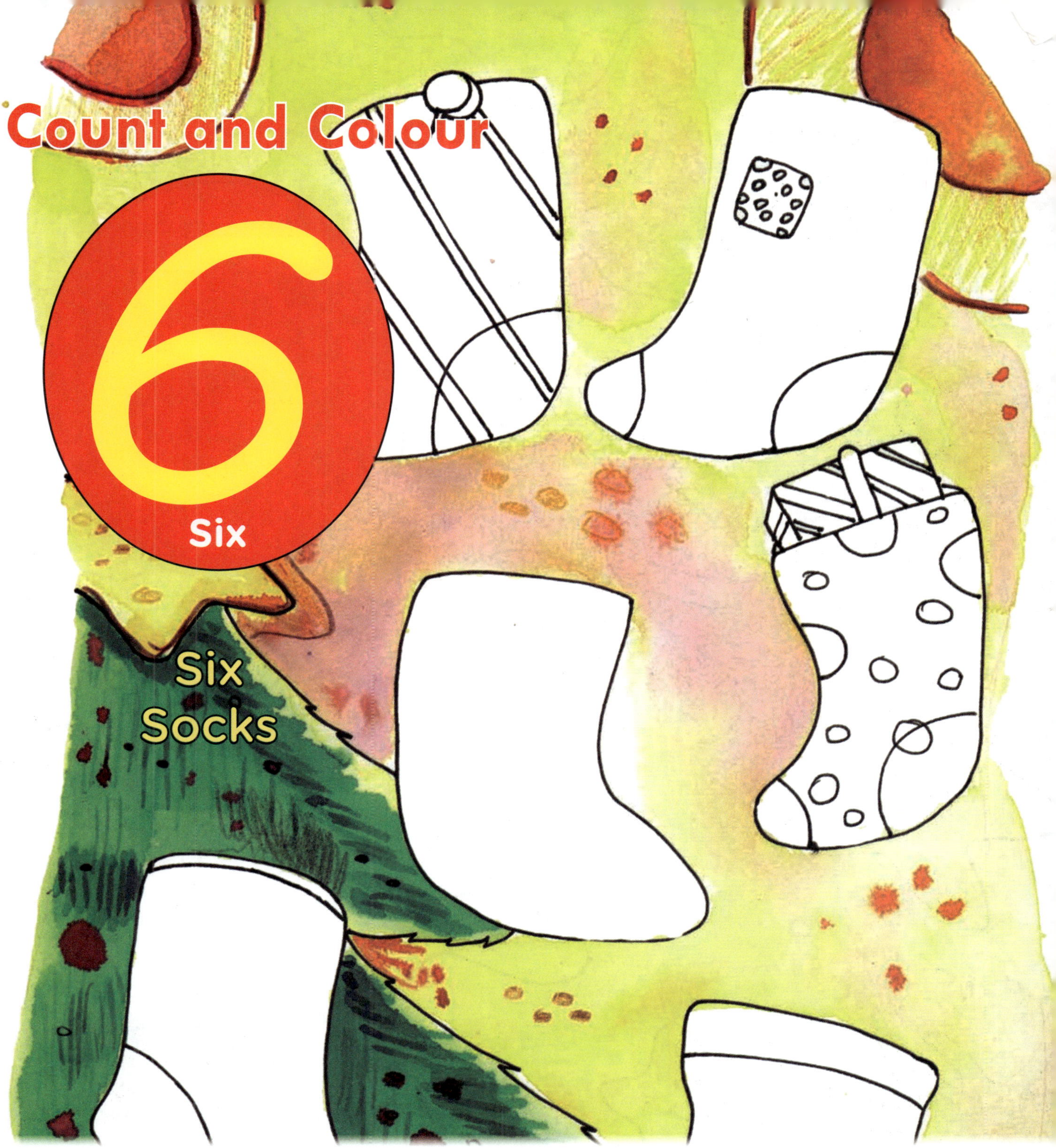

Trace and write :

6 6 6 6 6 6 6

6 6 6 6 6 6 6

6 6 6 6 6 6 6

6 6 6 6 6 6 6

Count and Colour

Trace and write :

7 7 7 7 7 7 7

7 7 7 7 7 7 7

7 7 7 7 7 7 7

7 7 7 7 7 7 7

Count and Colour

Trace and write :

8 8 8 8 8 8 8

8 8 8 8 8 8 8

8 8 8 8 8 8 8

8 8 8 8 8 8 8

Count and Colour

9

Nine

Nine Balls

Trace and write :

9 9 9 9 9 9 9

9 9 9 9 9 9 9

9 9 9 9 9 9 9

9 9 9 9 9 9 9

Trace and write :

10 10 10 10 10 10 10

10 10 10 10 10 10 10

10 10 10 10 10 10 10

10 10 10 10 10 10 10

Colour the number names. Then write them again in the space provided.

SIX ....

SEVEN ....

EIGHT ....

NINE ....

TEN ....

Look at the number on the left. Count and colour the same number of objects on the right.

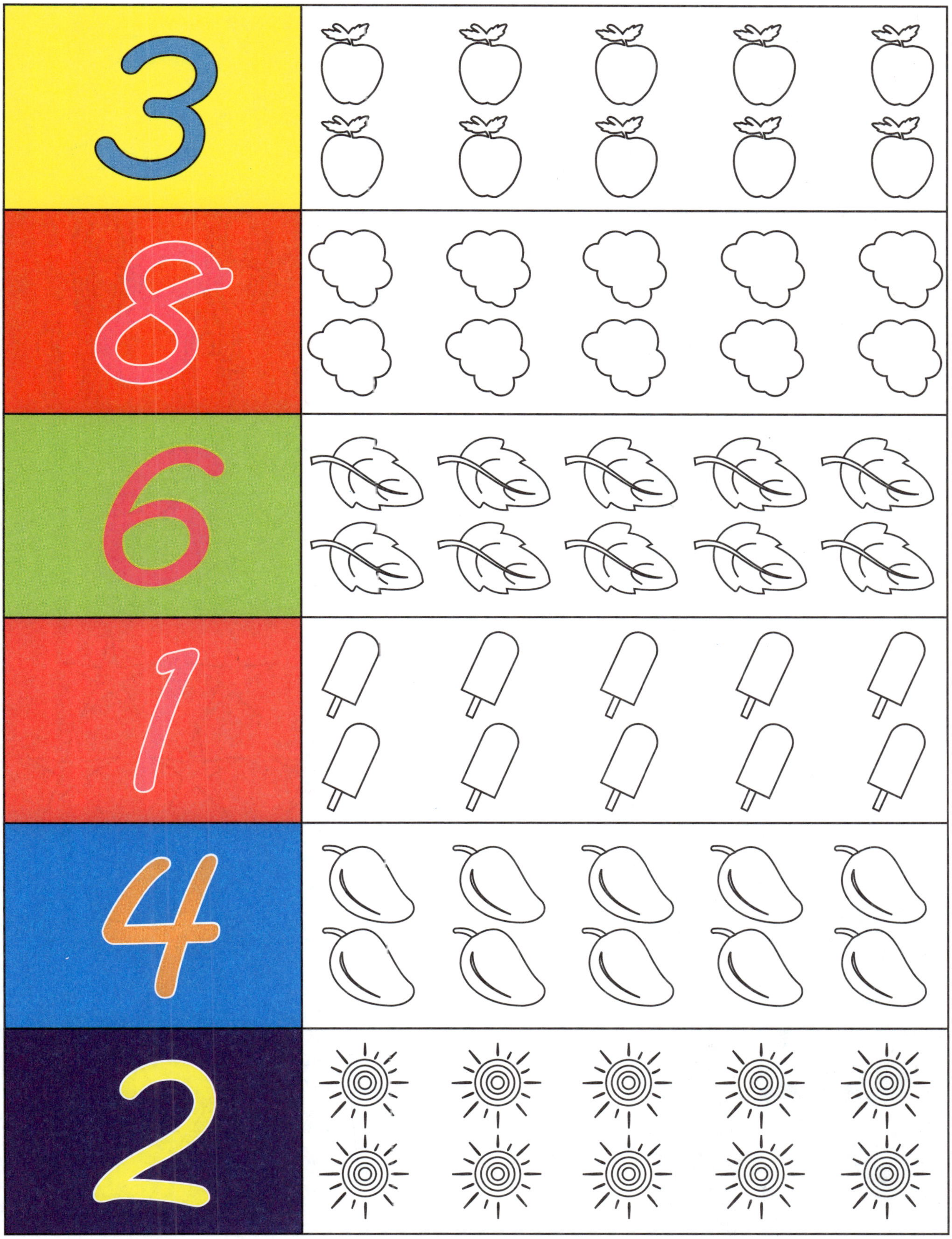

Look at the number on the left.
Count and colour the same amount of objects on the right.

Enjoy the number rhyme and have fun acting through it.

1, 2, buckle my shoe
3, 4, shut the door
5, 6, pick up sticks
7, 8, lay them straight
9, 10, a big, fat hen

1, 2, buckle my shoe

3, 4, shut the door

5, 6, pick up sticks

7, 8, lay them straight

9, 10, a big, fat hen

Circle every object that has 4 on it.

Circle every object that has 9 on it.

Throw these balls to their boxes. Match the numbers.

Count and write the numbers.

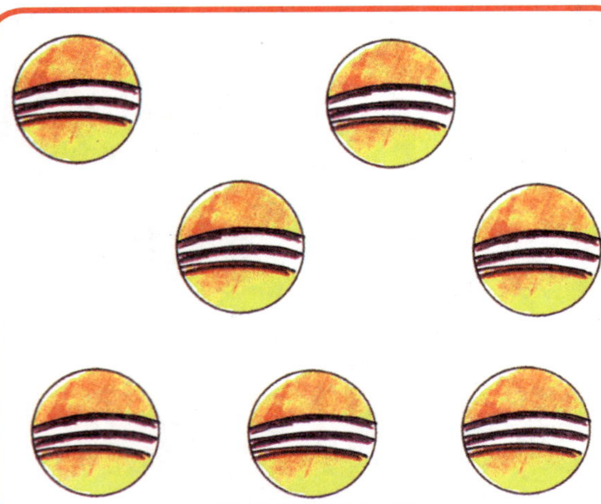

Draw a line from the number to the word. One is done for you.

4	THREE
6	ONE
1	EIGHT
9	SIX
3	FOUR
2	NINE
5	FIVE
8	TWO

Look at the following picture and tell :

- ☐ How many dwarfs are there ?
- ☐ How many chicks are there?
- ☐ How many flowers are there ?
- ☐ How many fish are there in the pond?
- ☐ How many rabbits are there ?

Colour the picture as per instructions.

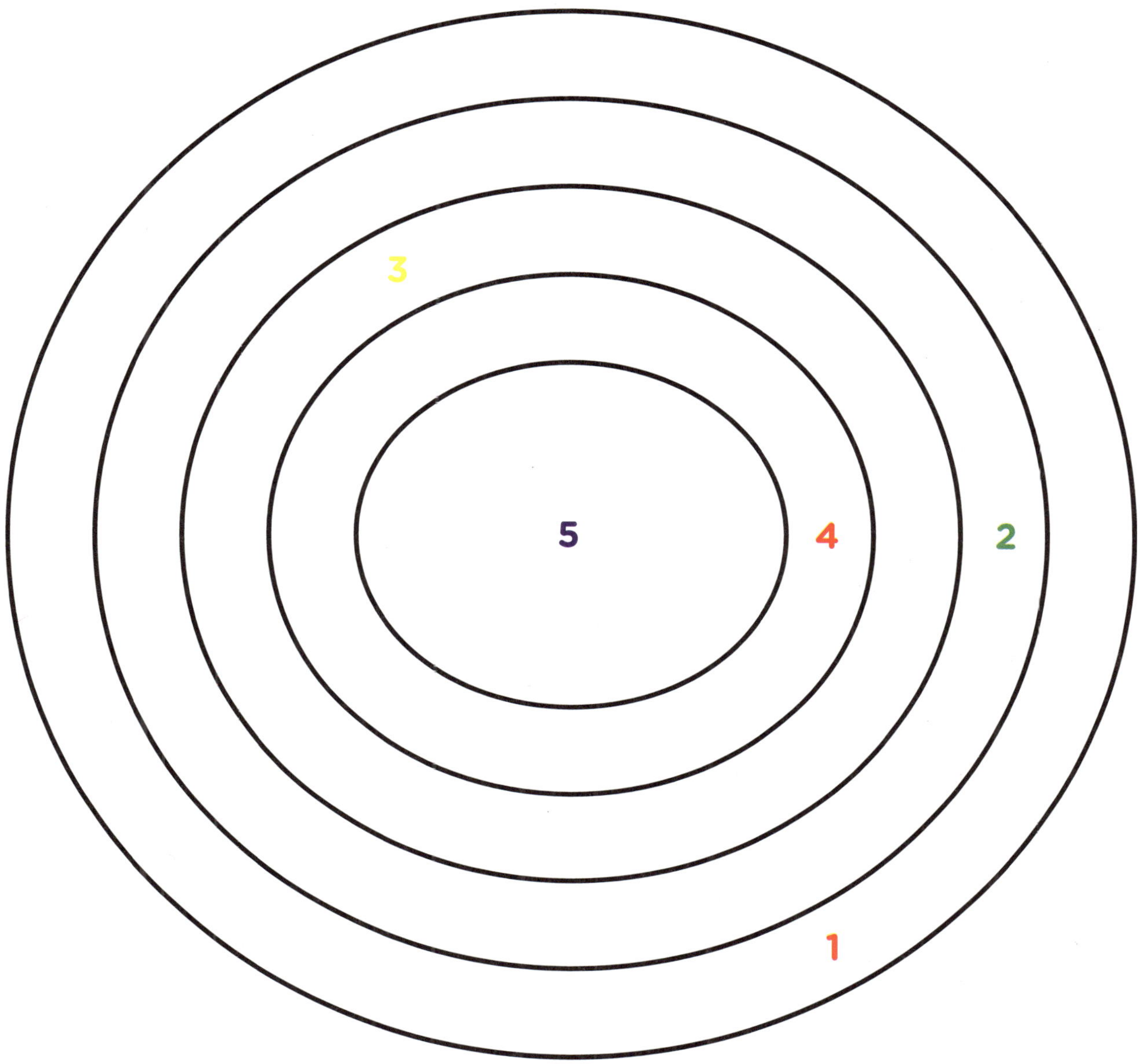

- Colour the biggest ring RED. Hint: it has 1 written on it.
- Colour the third ring YELLOW. Hint: it has 3 written on it.
- Colour the smallest ring BLUE.. Hint: it has 5 written on it.
- Colour the second ring GREEN.. Hint: it has 2 written on it.
- Colour the ring that is biggeer than smallest ring PINK. Hint: it has 4 written on it.

Learning to Count from 11 to 20

Numbers 11 to 20 have two digits- 11, 12, 13···

Numbers 10 to 19 have 1 followed by 0, 1, 2, 3, 4, 5, 6, 7, 8 and 9. Let us now learn to read these numbers.

10 1 makes 11

10 2 makes 12

10 3 makes 13

10 + 4 makes 14

10

5

makes 15

10

6

makes 16

10

7

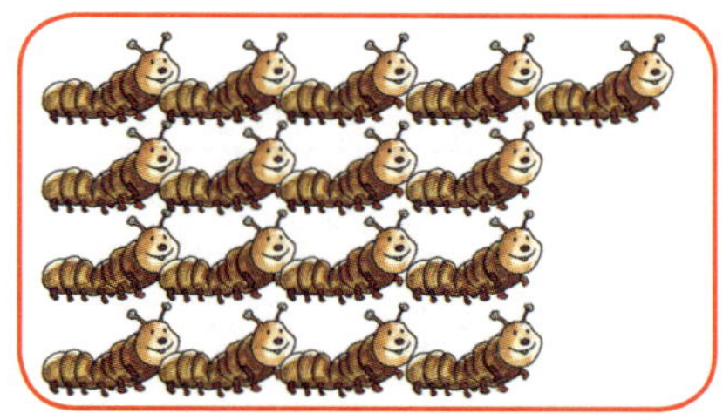

makes 17

10

8

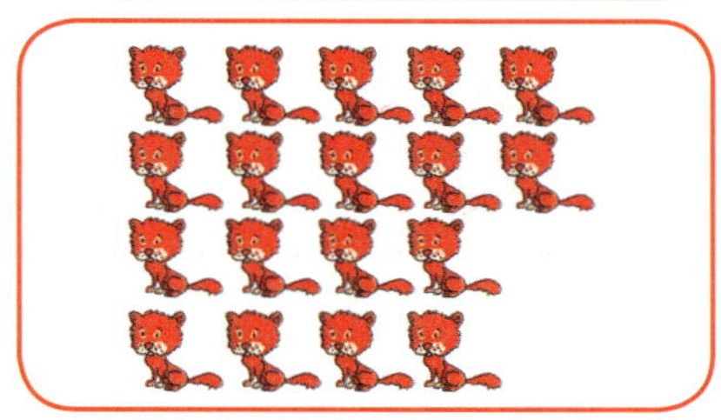

makes 18

10

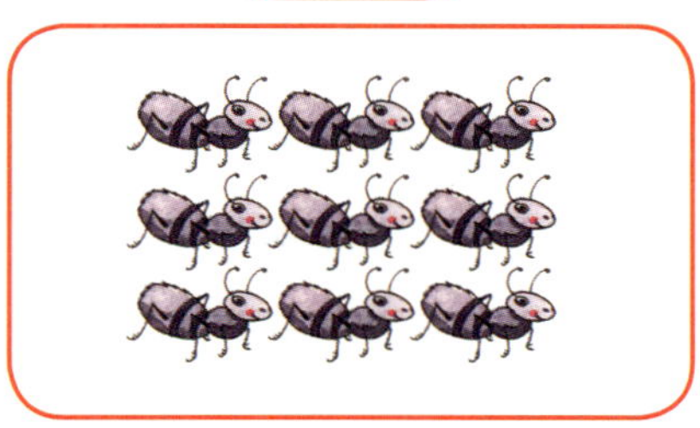

9

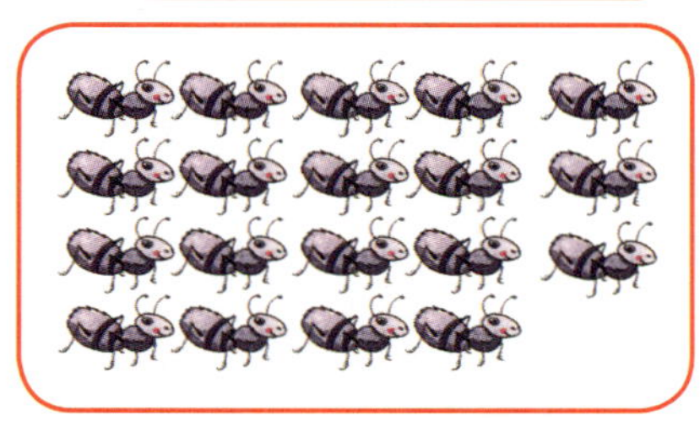

makes 19

10

10

makes 20

Writing and counting 11 to 20

(Teacher can ask the students to get 10 simple bindi packs in the class. The children should count the appropriate number of bindis and stick in the box given)

11 = Eleven

11 11 11 11

12 = Twelve

12 12 12 12

13 = Thirteen

13 13 13 13

14 = Fourteen

14 14 14 14

15 = Fifteen

15 15 15 15

16 = Sixteen

16 16 16 16

17 = Seventeen

17 17 17 17

18 = Eighteen

18 18 18 18

19 = Nineteen

19 19 19 19

20 = Twenty

20 20 20 20

Colour the counting from 1 to 10 to make elephant reach the ball.

1	5	6	12	6	19	1
11	2	9	13	7	15	12
13	3	0	6	19	12	4
15	1	4	5	9	5	7
16	19	12	9	6	3	15
8	6	7	8	12	7	6
9	4	9	16	13	8	9
0	1	11	14	6	11	10

Join the numbers from 1 to 20 to complete the picture and colour it.

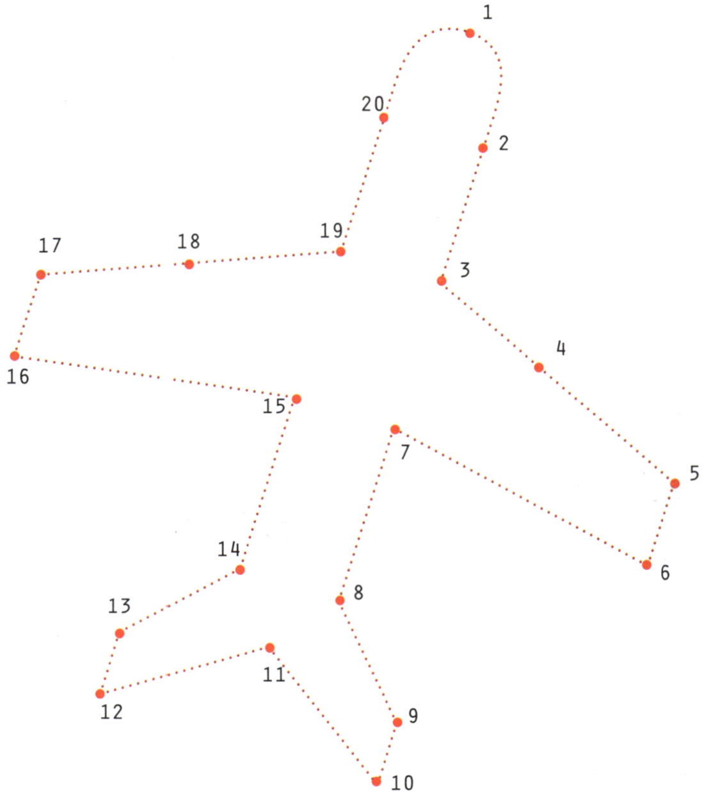

Fill in the blanks.

10

4

makes ....

10

6

makes ....

10

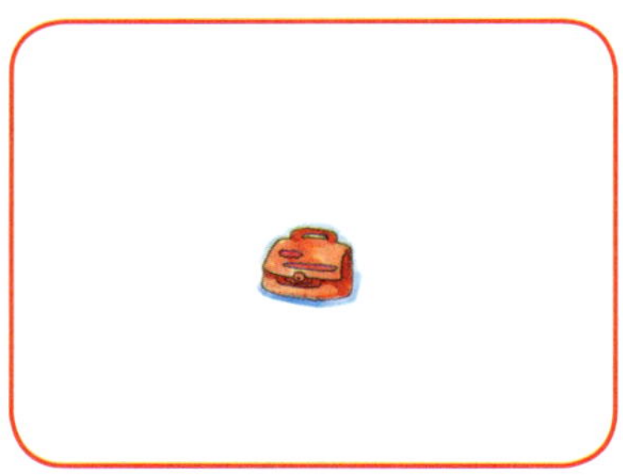

1

makes ....

10

8

makes ....

Fill in the blanks.

10 | 3 | makes ....

10 | 2 | makes ....

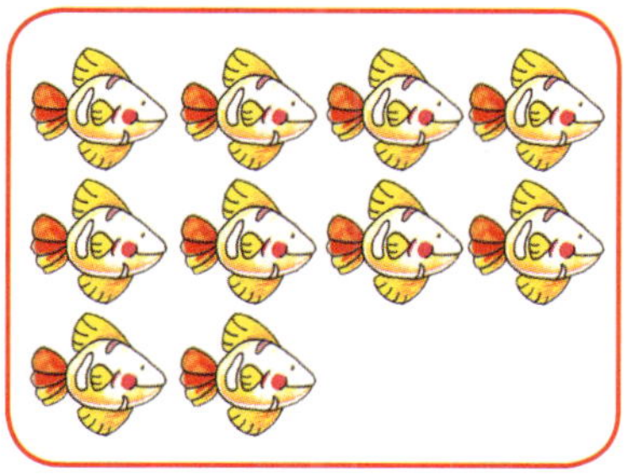 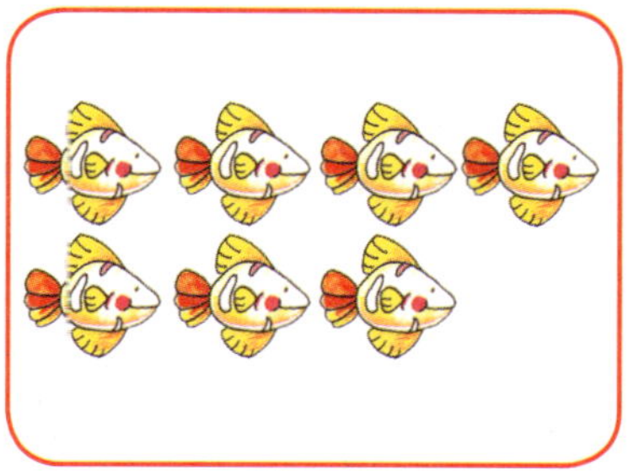 

10 | 7 | makes ....

10 | 5 | makes ....

Join the lines in order. Start from 1.
You can colour it too.

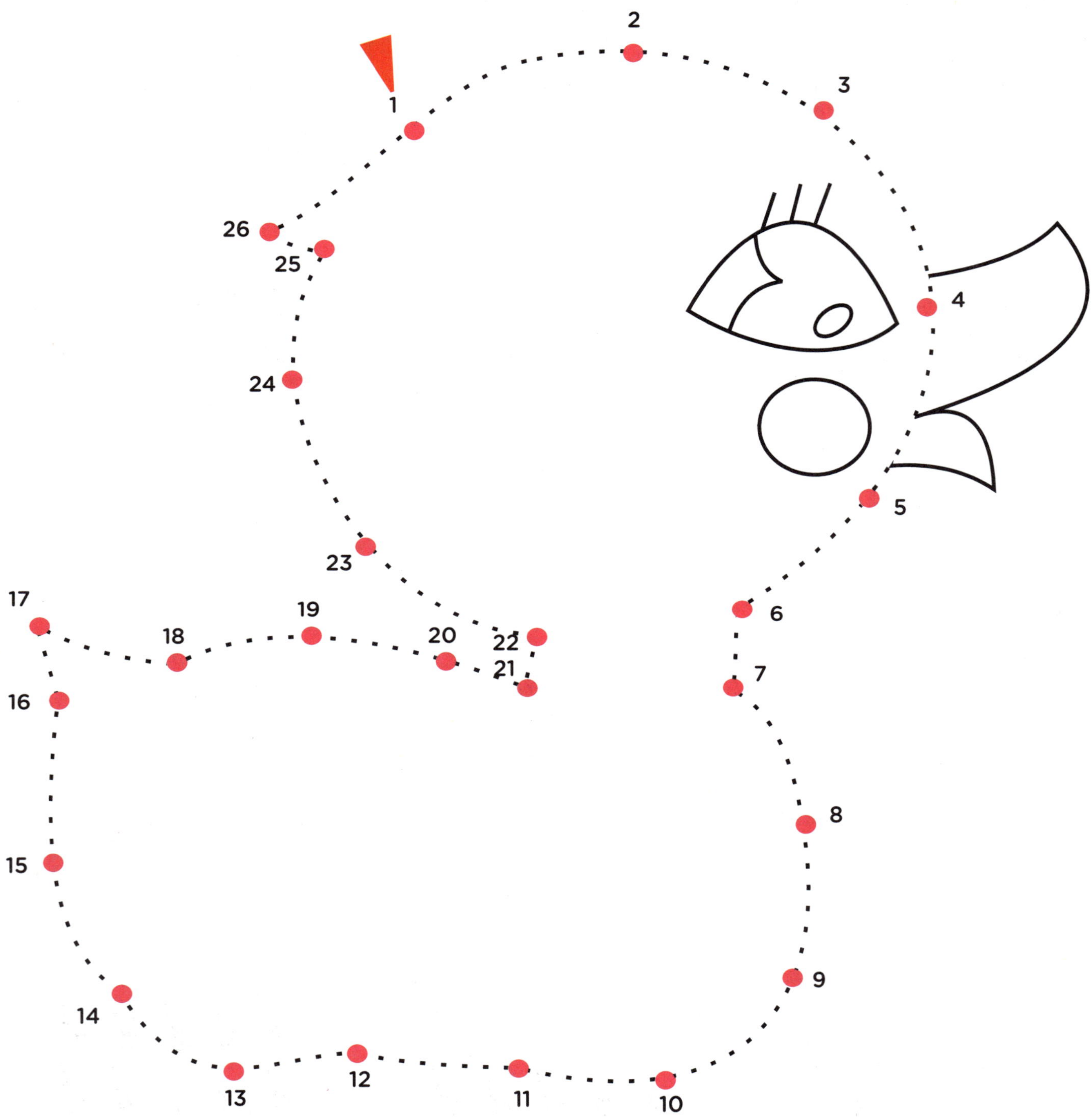

Write the numbers in blank boxes.

20	+	2	=	
20	+	4	=	
20	+	3	=	
20	+	5	=	
20	+	1	=	
20	+	9	=	
20	+	6	=	
20	+	8	=	
20	+	7	=	
20	+	10	=	

Fill in the numbers between :

2									11
9									18
7									16
3									13
1									10
20									29
31									40

Complete the grid

1		21		
	12		32	
				43
	14			
		25		
6			36	
	17			
				48
	19			
10		30	40	50

Fill in the numbers between :

1									9
10									19
20									29
30									39
40									49
50									59
60									69
70									79
80									89
90									99

100

Lets learn number names

1 One

2 Two

3 Three

4 Four

5 Five

6 Six

7 Seven

8 Eight

9 Nine

10 Ten

11 Eleven

12 Twelve

13 Thirteen

14 Fourteen

15 Fifteen

16 Sixteen

17 Seventeen

18 Eighteen

19 Nineteen

20 Twenty

Numbers up to 100

Read and learn

10	Ten
20	Twenty
30	Thirty
40	Forty
50	Fifty
60	Sixty
70	Seventy
80	Eighty
90	Ninety
100	Hundred

Fill in the missing numbers.

1		3		5	6	7	8	9	10
11	12			15	16		18		20
	22		24	25			28		30
31		33		35	36	37		39	40
41		43	44	45		47	48		50
51	52	53		55			58	59	60
61		63		65	66		68		70
71		73	74		76		78		80
81		83	84		86	87		89	90
91	92		94		96	97		99	100

Number Chart :

1	2	3	4	5	6	7	8	9	10
11	12	13	[illegible]	15	16	17	18	19	20
21	22	23	24	25	26	27	[illegible]	29	30
31	32	33	34	35	36	[illegible]	[illegible]	[illegible]	40
41	42	43	44	45	46	47	48	49	50
51	52	53	54	55	56	57	58	59	60
61	62	63	64	65	66	67	68	69	70
71	72	73	74	75	76	77	78	79	80
81	82	83	84	85	86	87	88	89	90
91	92	93	94	95	96	97	98	99	100